VERBS
by Mary Ellen Pierce

PAGE	TITLE	CONCEPTS AND SKILLS
1	That's a Verb!	Recognizing Verbs
2	Ready—Action!	Action Verbs
3	About the Subject	Linking Verbs
4	What's My Line?	More Linking Verbs
5	Helping Hands	Auxiliary Verbs and Phrases
6	Which Is It?	Action, Linking, Auxiliary Verbs
7	Is There a Receiver?	Transitive Verbs
8	What Follows?	Intransitive Verbs
9	Keeping Things Straight	Transitive and Intransitive Verbs
10	How Are They Formed?	Principal Parts of Verbs
11	How Are They Used?	More Principal Parts
12	Person, Number, Tense	Conjugation
13	Identification, Please	Using Tenses
14	Which Says It Best?	Choosing Verbs
15	A Verb and Its Relations	Verb Relationships in Sentences
16	Singles with Plurals Don't Mix	Subject—Verb Agreement
17	Verb Demons	Problem Verbs
18	These Cause Trouble	More Problem Verbs
19	Troublesome Verbs	Review I
20	General Review	Review II

This book targets *verbs* as a specific skill in Language Arts. The book includes activities for all types of verbs. The pages are designed to supplement any basal English program. Basic rules to remember are included on introduction pages. The pages may be used to assess students' current knowledge, to provide a quick review, a test, or a filler for those last few minutes of class time. They may be used for an opening exercise to get students in the "swing of class things." A substitute teacher will also find the pages most helpful.

The "Bull's Eye" logo on each page is a graphic way of showing each student's score. The logo also includes motivational messages for the students.

ANSWERS

When the answers WILL vary, no specific answers are given. When answers CAN vary, one option is given. The "Bull's Eye" logo on each page shows the possible score. Figure the remaining score according to your grading system and fill in. Color in the circle that reflects each student's score.

Page 1
1. loped
2. lost
3. discovered
4. broke
5. blew
6. trotted
7. flashed
8. coughed
9. snarled
10. cut
11. takes
12. crossed
13. painted
14. watched
15. gave
16. buried
17. rolled
18. slept
19. live
20. rained

Remaining answers will vary.

Page 2
1. ran, approached
2. received
3. went
4. gave
5. carried
6. tastes
7. read
8. sold
9. talked
10. hid
11. broke, fell
12. pulled
13. died
14. helped
15. jumped
16. gave
17. greeted
18. failed
19. shone
20. answered

Remaining answers will vary.

COPYRIGHT © 1987 McDONALD PUBLISHING CO.

Page 3

1. is	6. is	11. seems
2. tastes	7. were	12. is
3. were	8. smells	13. were
4. was	9. was	14. am
5. feels	10. are	15. was

1. am	5. tastes	9. was
2. are	6. seems	10. seemed
3. were	7. is	11. am
4. was	8. is	

Remaining answers will vary.

Page 4

1. dance	was		graceful
2. chess	is	game	
3. sport	is	tennis	
4. Jeanne	seems		happy
5. I	am		eager
6. girl	became		ill
7. woman	is	she	
8. ice cream	tastes		good
9. he	was	thief	
10. Thomas Jefferson	was	statesman	
11. these	are	foods	
12. teacher	is	Mr. Shultz	
13. West Indies	is	area	
14. you	look		beautiful
15. this	is	omelet	
16. class	appears		content

Page 5

1. was broken	11. did bring
2. are playing	12. was destroyed
3. were going	13. are playing
4. am presenting	14. was caught
5. have solved	15. will become
6. have seen	16. are taking
7. has been written	17. does smell
8. was dismayed	18. has been
9. is raining	19. was sent
10. had been tested	20. have been used

1. was	5. may	9. had
2. had	6. did	10. could
3. am	7. Have	11. does
4. had been	8. were	12. has

Page 6

1. L, is
2. A, won
3. L, seems
4. Aux, A, had won
5. A, wrote
6. Aux, A, will leave
7. L, seems
8. Aux, A, can count
9. L, were
10. A, bought
11. Aux, A, has been
12. L, were
13. Aux, A, will listen
14. A, scared
15. L, is
16. L, was
17. Aux, A, had made
18. A, cheered
19. Aux, A, did find
20. Aux, A, have written

Remaining answers will vary.

Page 7

1. made touchdown
2. watched parade
3. made sandwiches
4. reached cabin
5. screens were painted
6. gave dollars
7. broke window
8. cheered player
9. watch was found
10. car was parked
11. found child
12. America was discovered
13. thief was identified
14. examined cut
15. Emily was rescued

made		touchdown
watched		parade
made		sandwiches
reached		cabin
were painted	screens	
gave		dollars
broke		window
cheered		player
was found	watch	
was parked	car	
found		child
was discovered	America	
was identified	thief	
examined		cut
was rescued	Emily	

Page 8

1. birds migrate
2. soup is
3. John practices
4. sky is
5. stars are
6. did you eat
7. coat is hanging
8. Tiffany walked
9. did you finish
10. books are lying

1. is	9. is	17. are
2. is	10. sounded	18. hid
3. speaks	11. crashed	19. hiked
4. looked	12. cried	20. are
5. was	13. are	21. was
6. is	14. escaped	22. improves
7. stopped	15. was	
8. is	16. was	

TARGET VERBS

Page 9

T	wear	I	skates
I	sits	T	read
T	did, ride	I	came
T	gave	T	received
T	was pulled	T	was found
I	tastes	T	do, like
T	ate	T	caught
T	needed	I	is
I	is	T	poured
I	was	T	praised

Remaining answers will vary.

Page 10

watched, watched	went, gone
flew, flown	planned, planned
played, played	saw, seen
wanted, wanted	did, done
wrote, written	came, come
rang, rung	hid, hidden
began, begun	gave, given
planted, planted	called, called
rode, ridden	rose, risen
raised, raised	froze, frozen
wore, worn	grew, grown
swam, swum	sang, sung
sat, sat	became, become

drank	shown	sent	woven
worked	bought	risen	threw
moved	sold	knew	hung
left	guided	burst	sought
blew	driven	wrote	
lived	broken	thrown	

Page 11

1. has grown 5. chose 9. had shown
2. went 6. have known 10. jumped
3. worked 7. have fallen
4. has required 8. brought

1. gone 5. seen 9. began
2. traveled 6. become 10. kept
3. watch 7. went
4. guided 8. told

Remaining answers will vary.

Page 12

I eat	we eat
you eat	you eat
he, she, it eats	they eat

I ate	we ate
you ate	you ate
he, she, it ate	they ate

I shall eat	we shall eat
you will eat	you will eat
he, she, it will eat	they will eat

I have eaten	we have eaten
you have eaten	you have eaten
he, she, it has eaten	they have eaten

I had eaten	we had eaten
you had eaten	you had eaten
he, she, it had eaten	they had eaten

I shall have eaten	we shall have eaten
you will have eaten	you will have eaten
he, she, it will have eaten	they will have eaten

Page 13

1. 3rd person, past, singular
2. 2nd person, present perfect, singular
3. 1st person, future perfect, singular
4. 3rd person, past perfect, singular
5. 1st person, future perfect, plural
6. 1st person, present perfect, singular
7. 3rd person, future perfect, singular
8. 3rd person, present perfect, singular
9. 3rd person, past perfect, plural
10. 2nd person, present perfect, singular/plural
11. 3rd person, future, plural
12. 1st person, present, singular
13. 3rd person, past, singular
14. 1st person, past, plural
15. 3rd person, present, plural
16. 1st person, past, plural
17. 2nd person, present, singular/plural
18. 3rd person, past perfect, plural
19. 1st person, future perfect, singular
20. 3rd person, future perfect, singular

1. We will write letters.
2. He has given the correct answers.
3. I waxed the floors each month.
4. He will have left before sunrise.
5. I dreaded the business meeting.
6. I have aimed at the target.
7. They had played tennis daily.
8. I shall have reported by noon.
9. We smell fresh rolls.
10. They lived in the country.

Page 14
Answers will vary.
1. swarmed
2. whispered
3. spilling
4. stammered
5. flipped
6. yelled
7. trounced
8. lashed
9. roared
10. smashed
11. sizzling
12. dashed
13. smashed
14. hissed
15. belted
16. piled
17. rushed
18. sped
19. beat
20. lolled
21. stumbled
22. bolted

Page 15
2. Susan, S   made, V   brownies, DO
3. sun, S   is shining, V
4. Patrick, S   is, V   boy, PN
5. Dad, S   gave, V   dollar, DO   Tom, IO
6. Ann and Steve, S   are, V   tall, PA
7. we, S   saw, V   plane, DO
8. both, S   play, V
9. automobile, S   skidded, V
10. crowds, S   filled, V   streets, DO
11. aunt, S   teaches, V   ballet, DO   girls, IO
12. Joshua, S   was, V   happy, PA
13. men, S   played, V   checkers, DO
14. I, S   held, V   dog, DO
15. sliding, S   is, V   fun, PA

Page 16
1. doesn't
2. are
3. like
4. Are
5. is
6. have
7. come
8. was
9. aren't
10. need
11. was
12. was
13. don't
14. have
15. agrees

Remaining answers will vary.

Page 17
lie	lay	lain	set	set	set
lay	laid	laid	rise	rose	risen
sit	sat	sat	raise	raised	raised

1. risen
2. set
3. lying
4. sat
5. lain
6. rise
7. sitting
8. set
9. rose
10. Lay
11. sit
12. rose
13. laid
14. sit
15. laid
16. set
17. laid
18. rising
19. rose

Remaining answers will vary.

Page 18
bring	brought	brought
take	took	taken
learn	learned	learned
teach	taught	taught
let	let	letting
leave	left	leaving/left
shall	should	
will	would	
can	could	
may	might	

1. take
2. let
3. take
4. taught
5. let
6. take
7. let
8. may
9. will, may
10. taught
11. may
12. let, bring
13. bring
14. let
15. learned

Page 19
1. lying
2. sit
3. lay
4. Take
5. May
6. risen
7. sat
8. raising
9. shall
10. laid
11. raised
12. brought
13. sitting
14. laid
15. lie
16. can
17. laying
18. rise
19. set
20. will

Sentences will vary, but the verb forms should be as indicated.
1. taught
2. lain
3. raised
4. letting
5. would
6. may
7. sat
8. brought
9. learn
10. rose
11. laid
12. could
13. left
14. set
15. taken

Page 20
1. Sam, S   found, V   dollar, DO
2. Salmon, S   is, V   fish, PN
3. We, S   wrote, V   cards, DO   her, IO
4. you, S   were, V   agreeable, PA
5. Courtesy, S   is, V   trait, PN
6. wind, S   blew, V   roof, DO
7. Doris, S   gave, V   lessons, DO   her, IO
8. dress, S   is, V   beautiful, PA
9. you, S   will lend, V   book, DO   Ada, IO
10. grandparents, S   came, V
11. strawberries, S   taste, V   good, PA
12. prize, S   was, V   watch, PN
13. Empire State Building, S   is, V   tall, PA
14. teacher, S   gave, V   chances, DO   us, IO
15. they, S   are, V   team, PN

| devour | inquire | scribble | lounge |
| relate | strike | adore | scamper |

TARGET VERBS

Name   **Recognizing Verbs**

That's a Verb!

> The <u>verb</u> in a sentence shows action or state of being.
> EXAMPLE <u>Action</u> - Sue <u>swims</u> well.
> <u>State</u> <u>of</u> <u>Being</u> - Sue <u>is</u> a fine swimmer.
> The verb is always in the predicate of a sentence.

Underline the action verb in the following sentences.

1. The boy loped across the field.
2. Sue lost her bus pass at the game.
3. The lonely prospector discovered a gold mine.
4. I broke my front tooth eating taffy.
5. All night the wind blew fiercely.
6. The pony trotted across the corral.
7. Lightning flashed in the western sky.
8. Suddenly, someone coughed loudly.
9. My dog snarled at the stranger.
10. This afternoon I cut the lawn.
11. Penny takes tennis lessons.
12. The runners crossed the finish line.
13. Our class painted a mural for the school.
14. Dennis watched the neighbor's children.
15. The teacher gave the answer again.
16. The dog buried the bone under the bush.
17. The coin rolled under the sofa.
18. That tired old man slept.
19. Most raccoons live in North America.
20. It rained every day of our vacation.

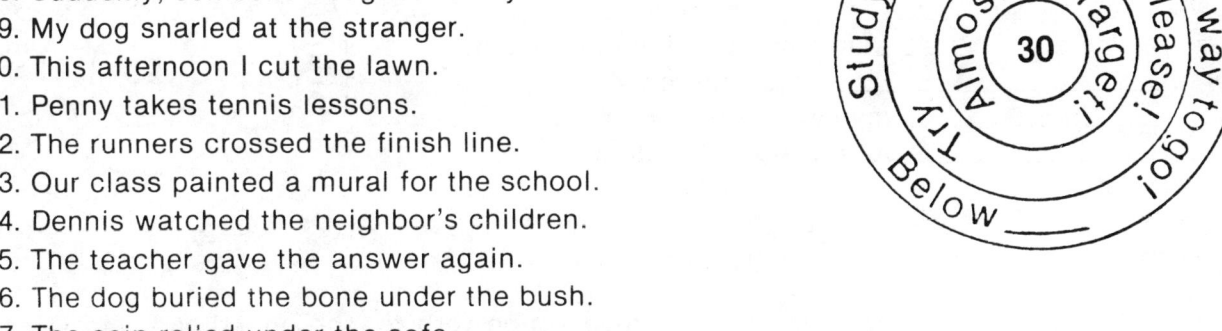

Choose ten of the sentences above. Circle their numbers. Rewrite each replacing the verb with another.

___

COPYRIGHT © 1987 McDONALD PUBLISHING CO.   1   TARGET VERBS

Name _____   Action Verbs

Ready — Action!

Supply an action verb in each blank in the following sentences.

1. The boys _____ quickly as the dog _____ them.
2. Ed _____ the gold watch for twenty-five years of service.
3. Ann _____ to the game yesterday.
4. Eileen _____ us the flowers as a gift.
5. Tom _____ the ball across the goal line.
6. Spaghetti _____ delicious.
7. I _____ a book about the pioneers.
8. The clerk _____ her several pairs of shoes.
9. Our teacher _____ to the class about himself.
10. Janet _____ the money in her shoe.
11. Andrew _____ his ankle when he _____.
12. The little boy _____ the wagon down the street.
13. The flowers _____ without water.
14. Mark _____ the fisherman haul in the net.
15. The horse _____ over the fence.
16. You _____ my sister too much food.
17. We _____ our guests at the door.
18. The experiment _____ twice.
19. The stars _____ brightly in the sky.
20. Dr. Peterson _____ the urgent call.

Rewrite the sentences below using a more descriptive action verb for the underlined verb in each sentence.

Sandy held her pom poms in her arms.
_____

The hungry dog ate the food in a hurry.
_____

The elderly man walked down the street.
_____

Martha took three apples from the basket.
_____

Tom said he found the buried treasure.
_____

Our puppy tore the newspaper before we could read it.
_____

The angry boy closed the door.
_____

COPYRIGHT © 1987 McDONALD PUBLISHING CO.   2   TARGET VERBS

Name _____   Linking Verbs

About the Subject

Linking verbs join the subject of the sentence with a word or words in the predicate that name or describe the subject.
EXAMPLE Patrick is the captain.
The roses are beautiful.

Underline each linking verb in the following sentences.

1. Connie is an outstanding student.
2. This hamburger tastes delicious.
3. My parents were upset with my report card.
4. The cave was dark and damp.
5. The breeze feels chilly.
6. That is my only answer.
7. We were early for the movie.
8. The apple cider smells bad.
9. He was only ten years old in seventh grade.
10. We are in the next game.
11. She seems happy with the dress.
12. The house is yellow with white trim.
13. They were glad about their vacation plans.
14. I am three years older than my friend.
15. Last year Tom was president of our class.

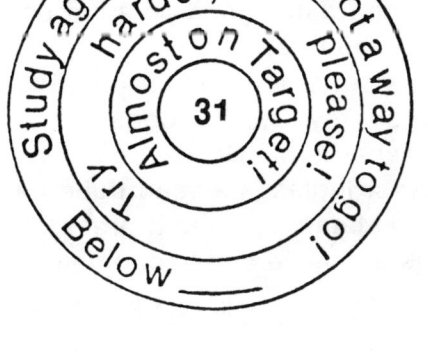

Choose a linking verb from the box to the right for each of the following sentences.

seemed	am	were
tastes	is	seem
seems	are	was

1. I _____ the star in the show.
2. We _____ hungry for pizza today.
3. We _____ happy after we won the game.
4. Last week I _____ late three times.
5. The candy _____ sour.
6. His apology _____ sincere.
7. The water _____ muddy today.
8. This _____ my favorite song.
9. The play we saw _____ funny.
10. Jan _____ ill after gym.
11. I _____ pleased with my gift.

Use each linking verb below in a sentence.

is _____
am _____
was _____
are _____
were _____

COPYRIGHT © 1987 McDONALD PUBLISHING CO.   3   TARGET VERBS

Name _____   More Linking Verbs

What's My Line?

The following sentences have linking verbs. Fill in the correct spaces in the chart at the bottom of the page using words from each sentence. "**A**" has been done as an example.

   A. He seems unhappy about something.

1. The dancer was graceful.
2. Chess is a great game.
3. My favorite sport is tennis.
4. Jeanne seems happy with her presents.
5. I am eager to go to the concert.
6. The girl became ill at the game.
7. The woman behind the counter is she.
8. Ice cream tastes good on a hot day.
9. He was the thief.
10. Thomas Jefferson was an American statesman.
11. These are my favorite foods.
12. My teacher is Mr. Shultz.
13. The West Indies is a beautiful area.
14. You look beautiful in that dress.
15. That is a cheese and ham omelet.

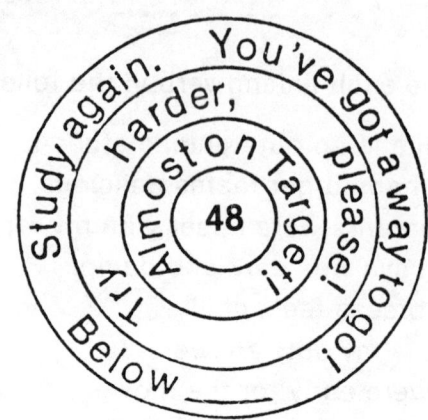

	SUBJECT	LINKING VERB	PREDICATE NOMINATIVE	PREDICATE ADJECTIVE
A.	He	seems		unhappy
1.				
2.				
3.				
4.				
5.				
6.				
7.				
8.				
9.				
10.				
11.				
12.				
13.				
14.				
15.				

COPYRIGHT © 1987 McDONALD PUBLISHING CO.   TARGET VERBS

Name _____ Auxiliary Verbs and Phrases

Helping Hands

> An auxiliary verb is a verb that helps another verb express meaning. A verb and its auxiliaries make a verb phrase.
>
> EXAMPLES is running   do shovel   have washed

Underline each verb phrase and circle each auxiliary verb in the following sentences.

EXAMPLE They (have) written a book.

1. The dog's leg was broken.
2. The children are playing in the snow.
3. Our parents were going to the movies.
4. I am presenting my project next week.
5. You have solved the mystery.
6. We have not seen that book.
7. The letter has been written in French.
8. Donna was dismayed at the news.
9. It is raining again today.
10. All the theories had been tested earlier.
11. Susan did bring her book to class.
12. Their house was destroyed in the storm.
13. John and Jack are playing basketball.
14. The mouse was caught in a trap.
15. A tadpole will become a frog.
16. Are you taking any books home tonight?
17. Does that pie smell good?
18. He has been a member of the Club for a year.
19. Sammy was sent to the principal's office.
20. Bicycles have been used for recreation and transportation.

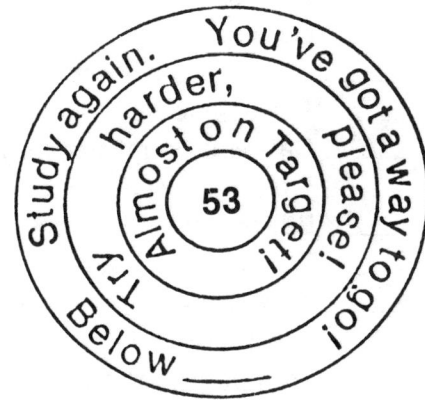

Use one of the auxiliary verbs from the box on the right in each sentence below.

1. Jack _____ sitting on the bench yesterday.
2. Susie _____ invited twelve friends to a party.
3. I _____ conducting a survey about the library.
4. He _____ _____ offered a job in the store.
5. They _____ visit our school tomorrow.
6. Our teacher _____ not find her glasses.
7. _____ you come to a decision?
8. The papers _____ flying around the street.
9. Why _____ he criticized our plan?
10. I wish I _____ play the piano.
11. How _____ it fit into the puzzle?
12. Sarah _____ changed her mind about dessert.

do	is
was	did
does	am
are	were
have	been
has	had
can	could
may	might

COPYRIGHT © 1987 McDONALD PUBLISHING CO.   TARGET VERBS

Name _____ Action, Linking, Auxiliary Verbs

Which Is It?

Underline the verb or verb phrase in each sentence below. On the line before it, write **A** (Action), **L** (Linking), or **Aux** (Auxiliary) to tell what kind of verb each one is.

EXAMPLE __A__ Someone <u>coughed</u> loudly.
__L__ She <u>is</u> at home.
__Aux,A__ I <u>was running</u> fast.

1. _____ Mr. Johnson is our speech teacher.
2. _____ He won his first match easily.
3. _____ She seems quite confident.
4. _____ Our team had won the championship.
5. _____ He wrote a letter to the newspaper.
6. _____ She will leave the party early.
7. _____ This game seems childish to me.
8. _____ Can you count the jelly beans in the jar?
9. _____ They were the grand prize winners.
10. _____ Bill bought his mother a present.
11. _____ The sky has been cloudy all day.
12. _____ Why were you late for class?
13. _____ The team will listen to their coach.
14. _____ Tom scared them with his scream.
15. _____ Mr. Wilson is the computer teacher.
16. _____ Sam was the star in Saturday's football game.
17. _____ Sally had made brownies for us.
18. _____ The fans cheered noisily for our team.
19. _____ Did Daniel find his new jacket?
20. _____ We have written the rules for the soccer game.

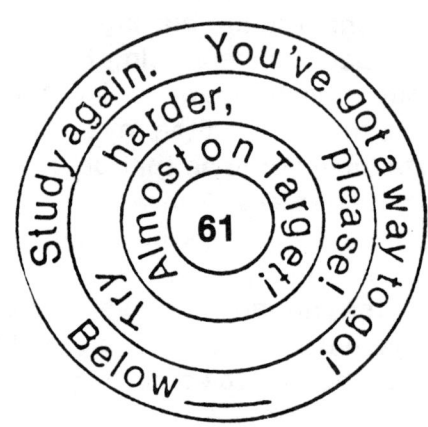

Rewrite each statement below as a question. Begin each one with an auxiliary verb.

Jay must practice his magic tricks several hours a day.

_____

I saw Mrs. Parker at the doctor's office with Jacob.

_____

Jimmy's dog came home late yesterday afternoon.

_____

Grandmother made my favorite cake for my party.

_____

Please lend me a dollar for lunch.

_____

COPYRIGHT © 1987 McDONALD PUBLISHING CO.   6   TARGET VERBS

Name _____ Transitive Verbs

Is There a Receiver?

Transitive verbs have a receiver of the action expressed by the verb.
EXAMPLES Frank ate the (pie).
The (pie) was eaten by Frank.

Underline each transitive verb. Circle the receiver of the action of the verb.

1. Tom made a touchdown in the big game.
2. Our class watched the parade on television.
3. Mother made us some sandwiches.
4. The hikers reached the cabin by nightfall.
5. The screens were painted by Jason.
6. Uncle Jim gave Josh ten dollars.
7. Andrew broke the window yesterday.
8. Each girl cheered her favorite player to victory.
9. My watch was found by Robert.
10. Somebody's car was parked on the lawn.
11. The officer found the missing child.
12. America was discovered by Columbus.
13. The thief was identified by Lucas.
14. The doctor examined the cut on his leg.
15. Emily was rescued from the burning building.

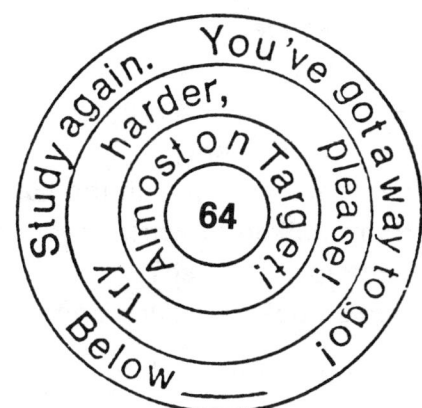

The receiver of the action may be the subject or the direct object of a sentence.

Use the sentences above to fill in the chart below. The first one has been done as an example.

| VERB | RECEIVER OF THE ACTION ||
	SUBJECT	DIRECT OBJECT
made		touchdown

COPYRIGHT © 1987 McDONALD PUBLISHING CO.   7   TARGET VERBS

Name _____   Intransitive Verbs

What Follows?

Intransitive verbs have no receiver of their action. They might show no action. Linking verbs are intransitive.

EXAMPLES The bell rang.
Sally is popular.

Circle the subject and underline the verb in the sentences below.

1. Some birds migrate in the winter.
2. Soup is good on a cold day.
3. John practices football everyday after school.
4. In daytime, the sky is different.
5. Stars are balls of hot gases.
6. Where did you eat?
7. Your coat is hanging in the hall closet.
8. Tiffany walked to school by herself.
9. When did you finish?
10. Karen's books are lying on the bed.

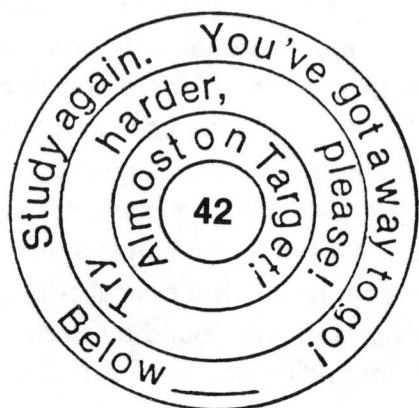

Write an intransitive verb to complete each sentence below.

1. He _____ both clever and popular.
2. The contract for the car _____ lost.
3. Sally always _____ softly.
4. David _____ everywhere for his sister.
5. I _____ successful in the contest.
6. That document _____ important to me.
7. The fire _____ at last.
8. One of these pages _____ missing.
9. Our plan for the picnic _____ the best.
10. The band _____ better than usual.
11. The cars _____ at the intersection.
12. Alison _____ about the loss of her kitten.
13. Your wet clothes _____ here.
14. The dangerous criminal _____ .
15. Her foot _____ very narrow.
16. The town _____ surrounded by police.
17. You _____ happier today than yesterday.
18. The dog _____ under the old porch.
19. We _____ to the crest of the hill.
20. These berries _____ not poisonous.
21. Meaghan _____ alone in the deserted building.
22. A storyteller _____ through practice and experience.

COPYRIGHT © 1987 McDONALD PUBLISHING CO.   8   TARGET VERBS

Keeping Things Straight

Underline each verb in the following sentences. On the line before each sentence tell whether the verb is **T** (Transitive) or **I** (Intransitive).

___ You wear the cutest clothes.
___ The cabin sits among the pine trees.
___ Did you ride your bicycle to school?
___ Mother gave Jennifer the new coat.
___ Danielle was pulled down the hill.
___ This bread tastes moldy.
___ Both boys ate a big breakfast.
___ The campers needed a better tent.
___ He is the man to see about the game's rules.
___ That was an important job.

___ Tom skates better than the other boys.
___ I often read her stories.
___ Those bananas came in this morning.
___ I received a call at midnight.
___ A pen was found under Jim's desk.
___ Do you like watermelon?
___ Michael caught five fish this morning.
___ One of these oranges is too sour.
___ I poured the sugar into the canister.
___ Mother praised us for our patience.

> Some verbs can be either transitive or intransitive.
> EXAMPLES The bell <u>rang</u>. intransitive
> Tom <u>rang</u> the bell. transitive

Use the following verbs in two sentences - once as a transitive verb and once as an intransitive verb.

published _____

won _____

played _____

drank _____

eat _____

knitted _____

run _____

read _____

smell _____

taste _____

Name _____ Principal Parts of Verbs

How Are They Formed?

Every verb has three principal parts: present, past, and past participle. An auxiliary verb always accompanies the past participle. Some verbs add ed or d to the present to form the other parts(A). Some verbs form the other parts with new words(B).

EXAMPLES
	Present	Past	Past Participle
A-	jump	jumped	jumped
B-	run	ran	run

List the principal parts of each verb below. Let the dictionary help you.

Present	Past	Past Participle	Present	Past	Past Participle
watch			go		
fly			plan		
play			see		
want			do		
write			come		
ring			hide		
begin			give		
plant			call		
ride			rise		
raise			freeze		
wear			grow		
swim			sing		
sit			become		

Write the correct verb form as specified below.

1. past of drink _____
2. past of work _____
3. past participle of move _____
4. past participle of leave _____
5. past of blow _____
6. past participle of live _____
7. past participle of show _____
8. past of buy _____
9. past of sell _____
10. past participle of guide _____
11. past participle of drive _____
12. past participle of break _____
13. past of send _____
14. past participle of rise _____
15. past of know _____
16. past participle of burst _____
17. past of write _____
18. past participle of throw _____
19. past participle of weave _____
20. past of throw _____
21. past participle of hang _____
22. past of seek _____

COPYRIGHT © 1987 McDONALD PUBLISHING CO. TARGET VERBS

Name _____ More Principal Parts

How Are They Used?

In the sentences below, underline the verbs in the past once; in the past participle twice.

1. Mr. Lindner has grown rich from his oil well.
2. Most people went to the annual fair.
3. These students worked very hard on the booth.
4. The injury has required lots of attention.
5. Tom chose Mark as his chemistry partner.
6. We have known about the plans for a long time.
7. You might have fallen from the ladder.
8. Sally brought cookies for a class treat.
9. Mrs. Young had shown her slides on China to her class.
10. Patty jumped out of the icy water.

Complete each sentence below with the correct form of the verb given in parentheses.

1. I have _____ to Aunt Mary's house. (go)
2. My family _____ to the east coast last summer. (travel)
3. We _____ that program every week. (watch)
4. Mom _____ us through the store. (guide)
5. I have never _____ that movie. (see)
6. Today, soccer has _____ a popular sport. (become)
7. They _____ to the game Saturday. (go)
8. My teacher has _____ us exciting stories. (tell)
9. When the movie _____ , we were quiet. (begin)
10. The librarian said we had _____ the books too long. (keep)

Write a sentence for each of the following words. Use the form indicated in parentheses.

work (past participle) _____

do (present) _____

grow (past participle) _____

start (past) _____

tell (past) _____

draw (present) _____

fly (past participle) _____

come (past) _____

wear (past participle) _____

blow (past) _____

creep (past participle) _____

sing (past participle) _____

COPYRIGHT © 1987 McDONALD PUBLISHING CO.   TARGET VERBS

Name _____ Conjugation

Person-Number-Tense

All forms of a verb are made from the three principal parts.

RULES:

1. Verbs have person - first, second, third
   Number - singular, plural
   Tense - different times

2. All person, number and tenses are shown in order when a verb is conjugated.

EXAMPLE: verb - play

Present

singular	plural
I play	We play
You play	You play
He, She, It plays	They play

Past

singular	plural
I played	We played
You played	You played
He, She, It played	They played

Future

singular	plural
I shall play	We shall play
You will play	You will play
He, She, It will play	They will play

3. Past participle forms are the same except they are used with an auxiliary form — have, has, had — to form the perfect tenses.

Conjugate the verb, EAT. Use all six tenses, all persons, singular and plural.

PRESENT — **PAST** — **FUTURE**

Singular	Plural	Singular	Plural	Singular	Plural

PRESENT PERFECT — **PAST PERFECT** — **FUTURE PERFECT**

Singular	Plural	Singular	Plural	Singular	Plural

(Target circle: You've got a way to go! Try harder, please! Study again. Almost on Target! Below — 36)

COPYRIGHT © 1987 McDONALD PUBLISHING CO.   Target verbs

Name _____   Using Tenses

Identification, Please

Identify the tense, person, and number of each of these verbs.

   EXAMPLE   I play <u>first person, present, singular</u>

1. it sprang _____
2. you have shrunk _____
3. I shall have played _____
4. he had won _____
5. we shall have gone _____
6. I have seen _____
7. she will leave _____
8. he has swum _____
9. they had known _____
10. you have run _____
11. they will give _____
12. I hide _____
13. she fell _____
14. we caught _____
15. they take _____
16. we chose _____
17. you grow _____
18. they had gone _____
19. I shall have played _____
20. she will have gone _____

Rewrite the following sentences using the tense indicated in parentheses.

1. We write letters. (future) _____
2. He gave the correct answers. (present perfect) _____
   _____
3. I wax the floors each month. (past) _____
4. He will leave before sunrise. (future perfect) _____
   _____
5. I dread the business meeting. (past) _____
6. I aimed at the target. (present perfect) _____
7. They play tennis daily. (past perfect) _____
   _____
8. I shall report by noon. (future perfect) _____
9. We smelled fresh rolls. (present) _____
10. They live in the country. (past) _____

COPYRIGHT © 1987 McDONALD PUBLISHING CO.   TARGET VERBS

Name _____   Choosing Verbs

Which Says It Best?

Some verbs are correct, but fail to give a vivid picture. List five vivid verbs for the ones below.
   EXAMPLE run <u>dash, race, lope, speed, scamper</u>

say _____
hit _____
go _____
breathe _____
work _____
tell _____
give _____
like _____
ask _____
move _____
eat _____
speak _____
walk _____
see _____

(Target graphic: Study again. You've got a way to go! Try harder, please! Almost on Target! Below ___ 92)

Write a vivid verb in each of the blanks in the sentences below.

1. The bees _____ around the hive during the summer.
2. "I didn't hear anything," she _____ softly.
3. You are _____ water all over the floor.
4. The witness was so nervous he _____ when he answered the questions asked by the lawyer.
5. The violent storm _____ the fishing boat over.
6. The coach jumped up and _____ , "Time!"
7. Our team _____ the other team by fifty points.
8. The waves _____ angrily against the wall of the pier.
9. Their heavy guns _____ for hours.
10. The mirror _____ into a hundred pieces.
11. The bacon is _____ in the frying pan.
12. John _____ quickly out of the room when the bell rang.
13. The racer, throttle wide open, _____ into the wall.
14. The angry cat _____ at the barking dog.
15. The batter _____ the ball over the fence for a two-run homer.
16. We _____ more logs on the dying fire.
17. The frightened child _____ into the house.
18. The winner _____ over the finish line three feet ahead of the next runner.
19. The torrential rain _____ against the windows.
20. We _____ on the sunny beach.
21. The thief _____ over the ladder in the dark.
22. The children _____ down breakfast so they wouldn't be late for the bus.

COPYRIGHT © 1987 McDONALD PUBLISHING CO.   14   TARGET VERBS

A Verb and Its Relations

Verbs may have these relationships in sentences:
Subject-verb-direct object... Andy took a picture.
Subject-verb-indirect object-direct object... I told Dad a lie.
Subject-verb... Jane ate after school.
Subject-verb-predicate nominative... The dog is a mutt.
Subject-verb-predicate adjective... The men are hungry.

Fill in this chart using the sentences below. The first one has been done as an example.

	Subject	Verb	Direct Object	Indirect Object	Predicate Nominative	Predicate Adjective
1.	lady	walked				
2.						
3.						
4.						
5.						
6.						
7.						
8.						
9.						
10.						
11.						
12.						
13.						
14.						
15.						

1. The lady walked rapidly down the street.
2. Susan made brownies for the party.
3. The sun is shining today.
4. Patrick is the boy at the counter.
5. Dad gave Tom a dollar for lunch.
6. Ann and Steve are tall for their age.
7. We saw the plane in the stormy sky.
8. Both of us play on the hockey team.
9. The automobile skidded around the corner.
10. Anxious crowds filled the narrow streets.
11. My aunt teaches little girls ballet.
12. Joshua was happy about his test results.
13. The old men played checkers in the park.
14. I held the dog for my sister.
15. Sliding down the banister is fun.

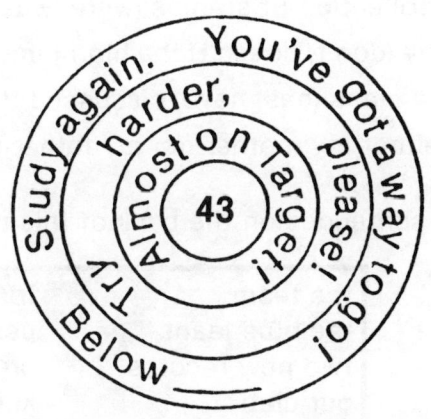

Name _____   Subject-Verb Agreement

Singles with Plurals Don't Mix

*A subject and verb must be the same number. (Remember, while subjects usually form plurals by adding **s**, verbs are usually made singular by adding **s**.) Check these rules.*

1. Use a singular verb with a singular subject.(A) Use a plural verb with a plural subject.(B)
    A. My leg hurts.   B. My legs hurt.

2. Use a plural verb with a compound subject having its parts joined by <u>and</u> or <u>both-and</u>.(C)
    C. Macaroni and cheese were in the recipe.

3. For subjects joined by <u>or</u>, <u>nor</u>, <u>neither-nor</u>, <u>either-or</u> the verb agrees with the nearer subject.(D and E)
    D. The man or woman is in charge.
    E. The man or three women are in charge.

4. A collective noun takes a singular verb if the group is a unit(F) and a plural verb when referring to individuals in the group.(G)
    F. The team is a winner.
    G. The team are wearing new uniforms.

Underline the correct form of the verb in parentheses in the sentences below.

1. Jack (don't, doesn't) come here often.
2. Jim and Alice (is, are) doing their homework.
3. Sandy and I (likes, like) to cook.
4. (Is, Are) the girls going to play soccer?
5. Two boys or a man (is, are) needed for the job.
6. The pupils, as well as the teacher, (has, have) gone.
7. Here (come, comes) the substitutes.
8. The pile of leaves (was, were) ready for bagging.
9. There (isn't, aren't) any chairs in this room.
10. Neither the bulb nor the batteries (need, needs) changing.
11. A flock of geese (was, were) flying south today.
12. A collection of stamps (were, was) on exhibit.
13. Why (don't, doesn't) the high jump and the broadjump begin?
14. The class (has, have) discussed the subject.
15. Neither my mother nor my father (agree, agrees) with me.

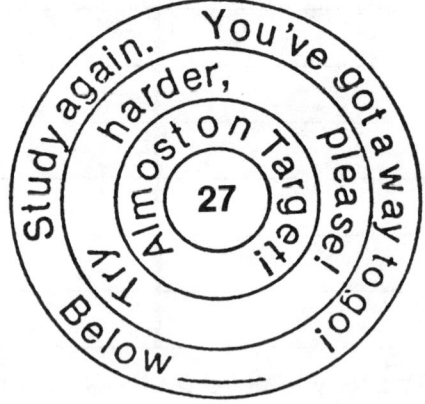

Write sentences on the back of this paper or on another sheet. Use the following subjects.

the team	fruits or vegetables	neither Dan nor Tom
the blue jeans	pens or a pencil	either Gary or Tina
two new records	breakfast and lunch	a pair of gloves
our club	knives and forks	the set of dishes

COPYRIGHT © 1987 McDONALD PUBLISHING CO.   16   TARGET VERBS

Name _____   Problem Verbs

Verb Demons

Three pairs of verbs that give trouble are lie-lay, sit-set, and rise-raise. List the principal parts of these verbs.

	Present	Past	Past Participle
lie	_____	_____	_____
lay	_____	_____	_____
sit	_____	_____	_____
set	_____	_____	_____
rise	_____	_____	_____
raise	_____	_____	_____

> Lie, sit, and rise are always intransitive.
> Lay, set, and raise are usually transitive and require an object.
> EXAMPLES   We lie here and rest.   I laid the book here.
>   She sits in that row.   She set the rock on the box.
>   The bread did not rise.   Did you raise the flag?

Underline the correct verb in parentheses in the sentences below.

1. The river has (risen, raised) two feet.
2. How long did you (sit, set) behind her?
3. You should be (laying, lying) down now.
4. As we (sat, set) there, the fog slowly (rose, raised).
5. These books have (lain, laid) there for a week.
6. The dough will (raise, rise) quickly in this warm place.
7. Lois is (sitting, setting) over there.
8. Won't you (set, sit) the cake on the table?
9. The wind (rose, raised) rapidly during the storm.
10. (Lie, Lay) your coats on the bed and (sit, set) here.
11. Won't you (sit, set) by me at the game?
12. Meat prices (raised, rose) last month.
13. Have you (laid, lain) those towels out?
14. I either (set, sit) and fish or (lie, lay) on the bank and sleep.
15. My work was (laid, lain) aside for dinner.
16. Sue (set, sat) the table before we (set, sat) down.
17. She has (lain, laid) the sweaters on the shelf.
18. Robbie's red face indicated his temper was (rising, raising).
19. The sun (rose, raised) over the mountains.

Write original sentences on the back of this paper or on another sheet using lie, lay, sit, set, rise, and raise correctly.

COPYRIGHT © 1987 McDONALD PUBLISHING CO.   TARGET VERBS

Name _____   More Problem Verbs

These Cause Trouble!

More troublesome verb pairs are bring-take, learn-teach, let-leave, shall-will, and may-can. Following are some rules.

1. Bring is used for action toward the speaker(A), and take is the reverse(B).
   A. Bring it to me.   B. Take the book home.
2. Learn is used to get knowledge(C), and teach is used to give instruction(D).
   C. We learn the rules.   D. I teach dancing.
3. Let is used to allow(E), and leave is used to go(F).
   E. He let me play.   F. I shall leave now.
4. Shall is used with the first person(G), and will is used with the second and third persons(H).
   G. I shall go.   H. He will go.
5. May is used for permission(I), and can is used for ability(J).
   I. May I play?   J. Can you read?

Fill in the blanks in the chart.

	Present	**Past**	**Past Participle**
bring	_____	_____	_____
take	_____	_____	_____
learn	_____	_____	_____
teach	_____	_____	_____
let	_____	_____	_____
leave	_____	_____	_____
shall	_____	_____	_____
will	_____	_____	_____
can	_____	_____	_____
may	_____	_____	_____

Underline the correct verb in parentheses in the sentences below.

1. When I go I must (bring, take) my books.
2. You should have (left, let) Sue use your tennis racquet.
3. Steve always forgets to (bring, take) his pen to class.
4. My dad (taught, learned) me to hike safely.
5. Will you (let, leave) me use your paper?
6. I didn't (bring, take) my uniform to the game.
7. (Let, Leave) me help you with that problem.
8. (May, Can) I go to the game with you?
9. You (shall, will) do as I say, or you (may, can) be sorry.
10. Experience has not (learned, taught) him anything.
11. Joanne, you (may, can) collect the papers.
12. (Let, Leave) me (take, bring) your book to you.
13. Will you (bring, take) me my sweater?
14. Mother, John will not (leave, let) me go with him.
15. I (learned, taught) to ski last winter.

COPYRIGHT © 1987 McDONALD PUBLISHING CO.   TARGET VERBS

Name _____   Review I

Troublesome Verbs

Underline the correct form of the troublesome verb in each of the following sentences.

1. How long have you been (lying, laying) there?
2. You can (sit, set) over there.
3. She (laid, lay) in the sun too long yesterday.
4. (Take, Bring) your homework home.
5. (Can, May) I please have a glass of water?
6. How much has the water in the dam (raised, risen)?
7. How long have you (set, sat) at this desk?
8. They are (raising, rising) the curtain now.
9. I (will, shall) see you after school.
10. The referee (laid, lay) the ball down on the line.
11. The crossbar was (risen, raised) by the official.
12. Tom has (taken, brought) the book to me.
13. Who has been (sitting, setting) in my chair?
14. The butcher (laid, lay) the knife on the table.
15. Don't (lay, lie) on my bed.
16. I (may, can) climb that pole without help.
17. The workmen are (laying, lying) tile today.
18. Oil will (rise, raise) to the top of the water.
19. Who (set, sat) his glass on this paper?
20. He (shall, will) visit them next month.

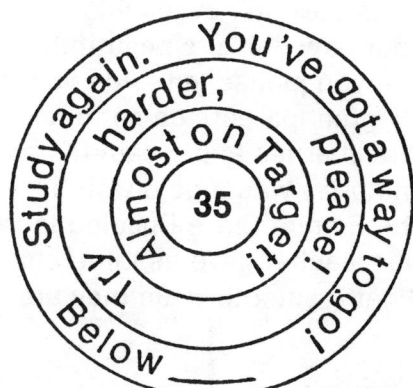

Write sentences using the correct principal part of the verb that is indicated.

1. teach (past) _____
2. lie (past participle) _____
3. raise (past) _____
4. let (past participle) _____
5. will (past) _____
6. may (present) _____
7. sit (past participle) _____
8. bring (past) _____
9. learn (present) _____
10. rise (past) _____
11. lay (past participle) _____
12. can (past) _____
13. leave(past) _____
14. set (present) _____
15. take (past participle) _____

COPYRIGHT © 1987 McDONALD PUBLISHING CO.   TARGET VERBS

Name _____ Review II

General Review

Fill in the information on the chart using the sentences below.

1. Sam found a dollar in the garbage.
2. Salmon is my favorite dish.
3. We wrote her get-well letters.
4. Were you agreeable to our plan?
5. Courtesy is a trait we need.
6. The wind blew the roof off our house.
7. Doris gave her swimming lessons.
8. Your new dress is beautiful.
9. Will you please lend Ada your math book.
10. My grandparents came to our house yesterday.
11. Strawberries and cream tastes good.
12. The prize was a gold watch.
13. The Empire State Building is tall.
14. Our teacher gave us three chances to succeed.
15. What a smooth team they are.

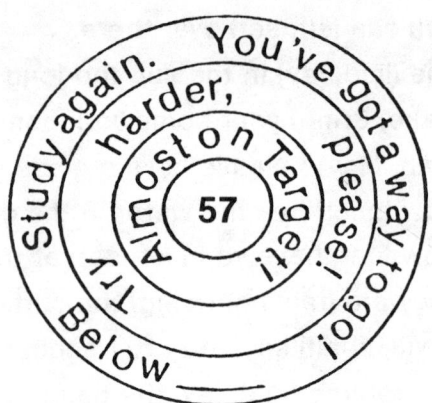

	Subject	Verb	Direct Object	Indirect Object	Predicate Nominative	Predicate Adjective
1.						
2.						
3.						
4.						
5.						
6.						
7.						
8.						
9.						
10.						
11.						
12.						
13.						
14.						
15.						

Each verb below has a vivid verb listed after it. Unscramble the letters in the vivid verb and write it on the line.

1. eat (vuedor) _____
2. tell (treale) _____
3. ask (requiin) _____
4. hit (reikst) _____

5. write (belricbs) _____
6. love (reado) _____
7. sit (negoul) _____
8. run (recpams) _____

COPYRIGHT © 1987 McDONALD PUBLISHING CO. TARGET VERBS